JUNGLE MAZES

Roger Moreau

Sterling Publishing Co., Inc.
New York

CIP Data Available

10 9 8 7 6 5 4

Published by Sterling Publishing Company, Inc.
387 Park Avenue South, New York, N.Y. 10016

Distributed in Canada by Sterling Publishing
c/o Canadian Manda Group,One Atlantic Avenue, Suite 105
Toronto, Ontario, Canada M6k 3E7
Distributed in Great Britain and Europe by Cassell PLC
Wellington House, 125 Strand, London WC2R OBB, England
Distributed in Australia by Capricorn Link (Australia) Pty. Ltd.
P.O. Box, 6651, Baulkham Hills, Business Centre, NSW 2153, Australia
Manufactured in the United States of America

Sterling ISBN 0-8069-0876-9

CONTENTS

A Note on the Suggested Use of This Book

As you work your way through the pages of this book, use a pointer rather than a marker. This will enable you to take the journey over and over again and will give your friends a chance to take the journey without showing them the routes you took.

Special warning: If the journey appears too difficult, avoid the temptation of starting at the end and working your way backwards. This technique would be a violation of the rules and could result in a severe reprimand.

COVER MAZE: Climb the roots and vines of this rain forest tree to reach the canopy above. You can cross from root to root and from vine to vine but do not disturb the wildlife.

INTRODUCTION

The great imaginary circle around the earth that lies halfway between the North and South poles is known as the equator. Here, days and nights are always of almost equal length, about 12 hours each along the equator. In most regions, the temperatures are hot and humid. Here are found the great rain forests, or jungles, of the world—in Central and South America, Africa, and Southeast Asia. One third of the world's land, or 15 million square miles, is jungle.

These jungles are filled with an abundant variety of friendly and unfriendly plants, insects, wildlife and people. The variety is so abundant that a great number of species are rarely seen and an equal number are still undiscovered. It is a fact that a lot of the known life benefits the human family in many ways. It needs to be protected and preserved.

A great deal still needs to be learned about these jungles. More exploration is needed. This is where the people of the world would like to call upon you. If you volunteer to go forth into the jungles ahead, it will be a great opportunity for you to do good for mankind. You will explore and photograph rare and unknown species. You will experience the thrill of discovery. It will be important for you to observe and note carefully the things that you see. But, be cautioned: It will require determination and uncommon courage. You will have to face much dangerous wildlife and many life-threatening situations.

GOOD LUCK!

THE JUNGLES OF CENTRAL AND SOUTH AMERICA

The jungles of Central and South America contain an enormous variety of plants and wildlife. It is believed that nearly one third of all the earth's species live in these jungles. Many of these species remain unnamed and unknown. Now you are ready to seek out, observe and study some of the rarest ones.

Starting Up the Amazon

To reach the jungle, start up the Amazon River by finding your way to where the river narrows.

Alligator Alley

Here, the river narrows and the anxious welcome that awaits you looks pretty dangerous. Avoid the alligators and work your way upstream and into the jungle.

The Top of the Rain Forest

This rain forest tree is full of wildlife. Ascend the vines to the top. You can move from vine to vine where they cross, but you must avoid disturbing the wildlife.

The World of Birds

There are many rare birds in these trees. Try to reach the unknown bird at the end

of this maze by ascending the vines and branches. You can move from vine to vine where they cross, but avoid vines blocked by birds.

The Frog Pond

This pond has several rare frogs in it and one that has never been seen before. You can get to him by moving from lily pad to lily pad. They must be touching for you

to advance. Don't worry about any frogs that are on lily pads and don't fall in.

The Butterfly Chase

Beautiful butterflies! Everyone loves butterflies. To get to that rare one on the

right, move along a single vine. You can go under and over other vines, but you cannot move from one to another.

Stalking The Jaguar

The jaguar is an endangered species. You are lucky to have spotted two resting in

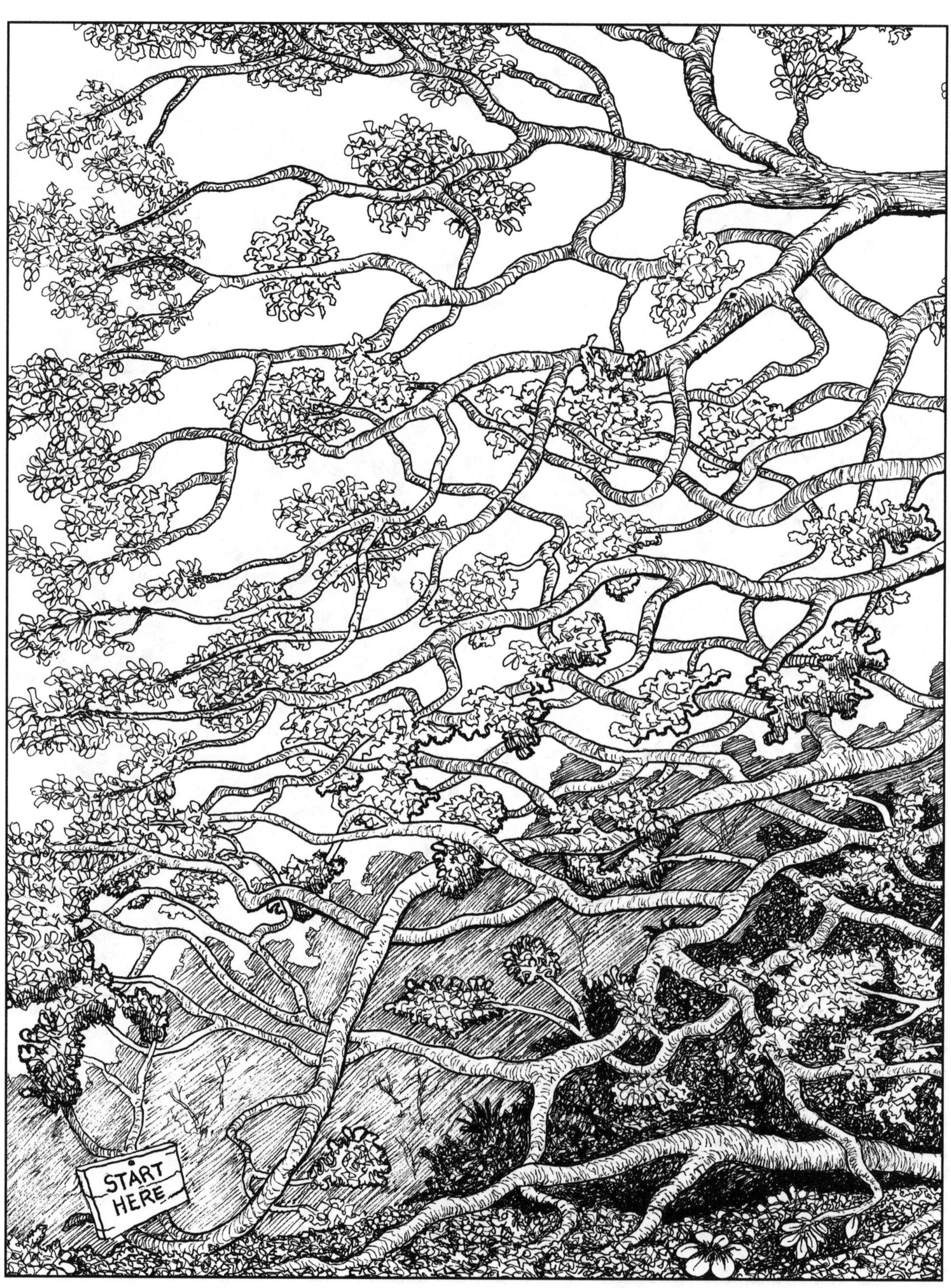

this tree. Work your way up the branches and get a photo. You can cross from branch to branch where they cross but not where leaves block the way.

THE JUNGLES OF AFRICA

Wildlife in the jungles of Africa is as abundant and varied as in Central and South America. It is also quite different. Zaire holds one-tenth of the world's total rain forest and in the remote regions of the Congo, the rain forests are virtually undisturbed by the encroachment of man.

The Road to the Jungle

To get to the jungle, hike down the road, avoiding the wildlife in the valley below.

The Gorilla Family

That's the mother gorilla checking out your camera equipment and the father overseeing the family and some of the neighbor's children. Get out your camera

equipment, for a picture of the mother and continue up the trail to get one of the father. Do not disturb the children or the parents might not like it.

Spiders, Spiders

Spiders! Everyone hates spiders—except you. To observe that rare one in the

upper right, climb the spiderwebs by moving along where they are not blocked by spiders. Be careful not to get stuck on this maze. It could prove dangerous.

The Golden Potto

Study the rare Golden Potto by ascending the vines. You can cross from vine to vine and move along the branch at the top. Avoid the bugs.

Jungle Photo Trip

This is a real photo opportunity. Much of Africa's wildlife can been seen in this jungle area. Find a clear path to the top of the hill and don't save on film.

The Elephant Herd

That herd of elephants on the ridge appears to be unaware of you. But one big bull

is starting to charge down the hill. Wouldn't it be a great chance to observe, close up, a charging elephant? Find a clear path up the trail. You'd better hurry.

Monkey Business

To get up into this rain forest tree and observe the wildlife, you hung these ropes. Do you think it was a good idea? It looks as if the monkeys and chimpanzees have

taken over. Now, you can't just climb any rope; you must avoid the monkeys and chimps to get up.

THE JUNGLES OF SOUTHEAST ASIA

The jungles of Southeast Asia are as unique and diversified as any of the jungles of the world. Some parts of New Guinea are so remote that they are rarely if ever explored. One can just imagine the variety of undiscovered animal species and the historical finds that most assuredly exist there. Many brave men have made attempts to find out. Some have returned to log their finds. Others were never seen again.

A Clear Path

If you have any misgivings about the jungle ahead, take heart. Notice that there is a welcome sign. All you have to do is find a clear path to the entrance.

The Temple of Angkor

Visit the temple ruins of Angkor. The statues of the gods are overgrown with jungle vines. To explore the temple, climb the vines. You can move along from vine

to vine except where they are blocked by leaves.

Inside the Temple

Most of the roof of this temple has collapsed. Find a clear path and exit through the door at the far end.

Snakes and Roots

No matter how you feel about snakes, don't let this chance slip to observe that big one in the tree. Climb from root to root but avoid the other snakes at all costs.

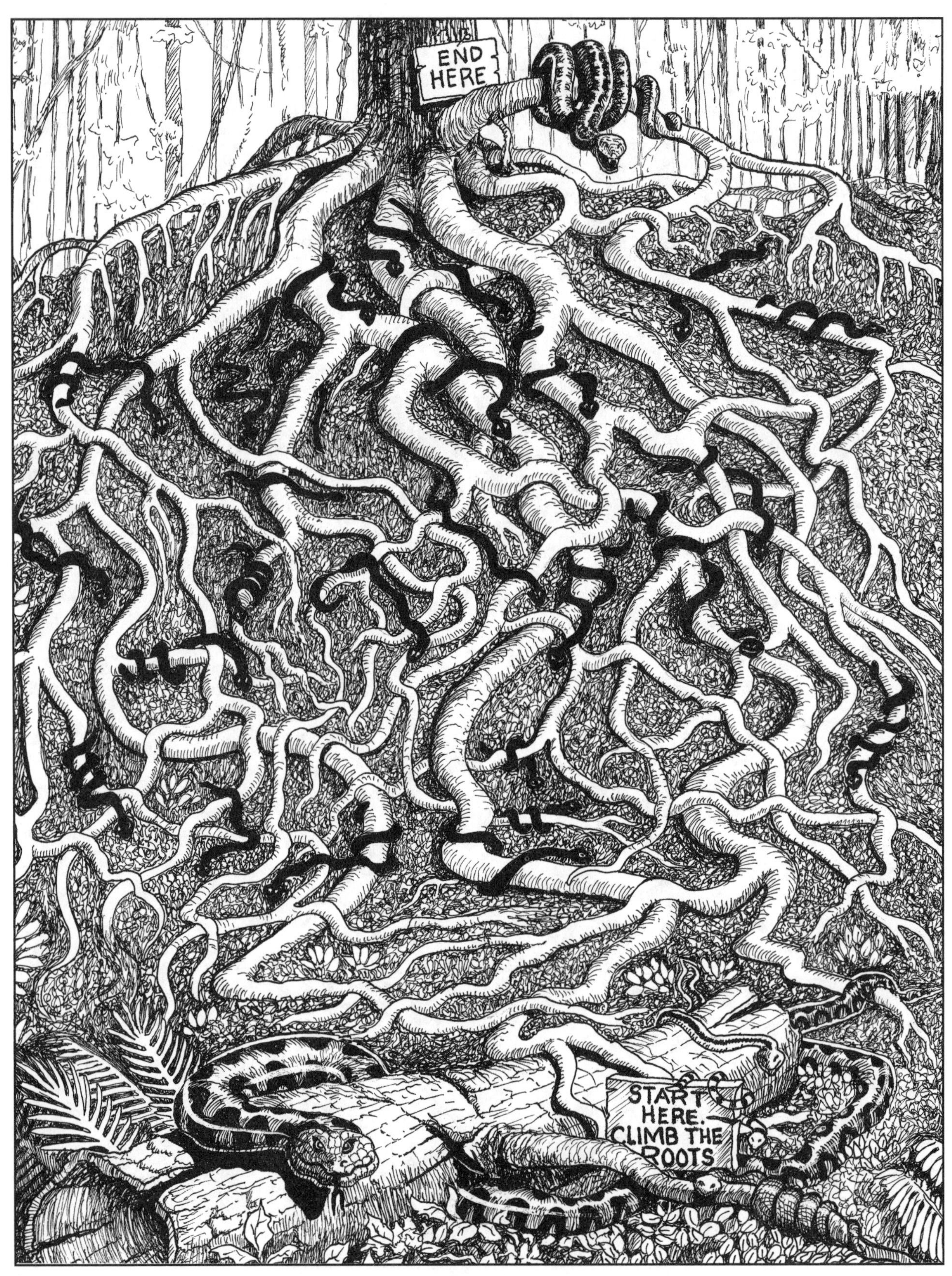

Looking for Lizards

There's a lizard at the bottom of this hill. It looks pretty safe, so find a clear path down and get a photo. Keep your eyes open for any signs of danger.

The Crossroads

There seems to be a crossroads ahead where you must make an important deci-

sion as to which way to go. It's up to you. But before you decide, look things over carefully. Either way, you must find a clear path.

Out of the Jungle

You have chosen wisely. Now take a boat down the river to civilization. Don't go over any falls.

WELCOME
DOCK HERE
FOOD MART
HOT DOGS
PLAZA MALL
AIRPORT LIMO

CONGRATULATIONS

Your discoveries have been made and the photos you took will be studied for years. It is very likely that new cures and scientific breakthroughs will occur as a result of the sacrifices and hardships that you had to endure to achieve such great success. There is no question that during your expedition your life was in danger, and yet you did not give up. You did not quit when the going got tough. When you were lost, you found your way. It is apparent that you took your responsibilities seriously, because you were careful to observe the smallest details along the way. This was not easy, and yet you did it. In fact, you have done so well that you will probably be called on again for some future task, possibly more difficult than this.

JUNGLE GUIDES

If you had any trouble finding your way through the mazes in this book, use the jungle guides on the following pages. These guides should be used only in case of an emergency.

Starting Up the Amazon

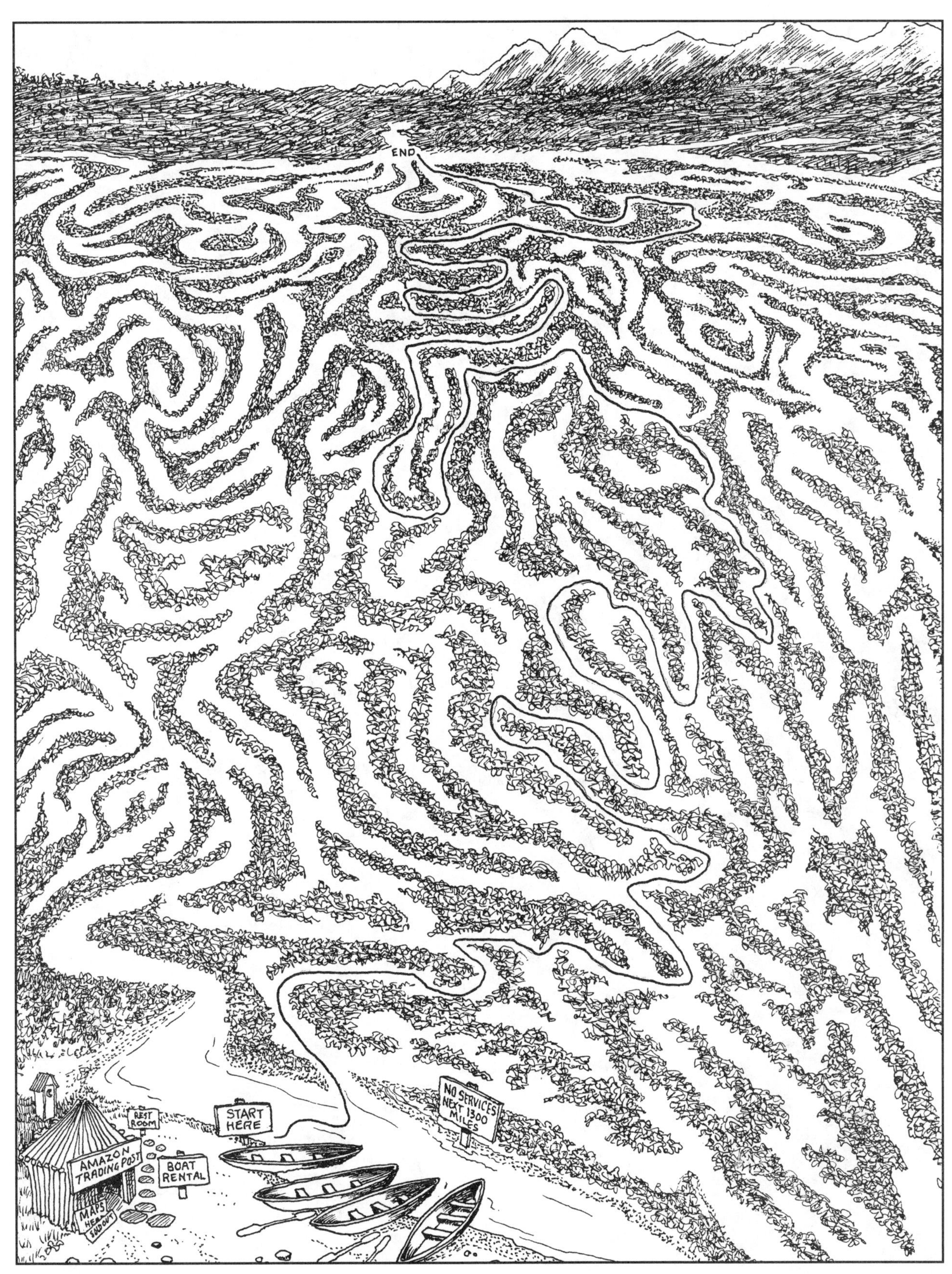

Alligator Alley

The Top of the Rain Forest

START
END

The Frog Pond

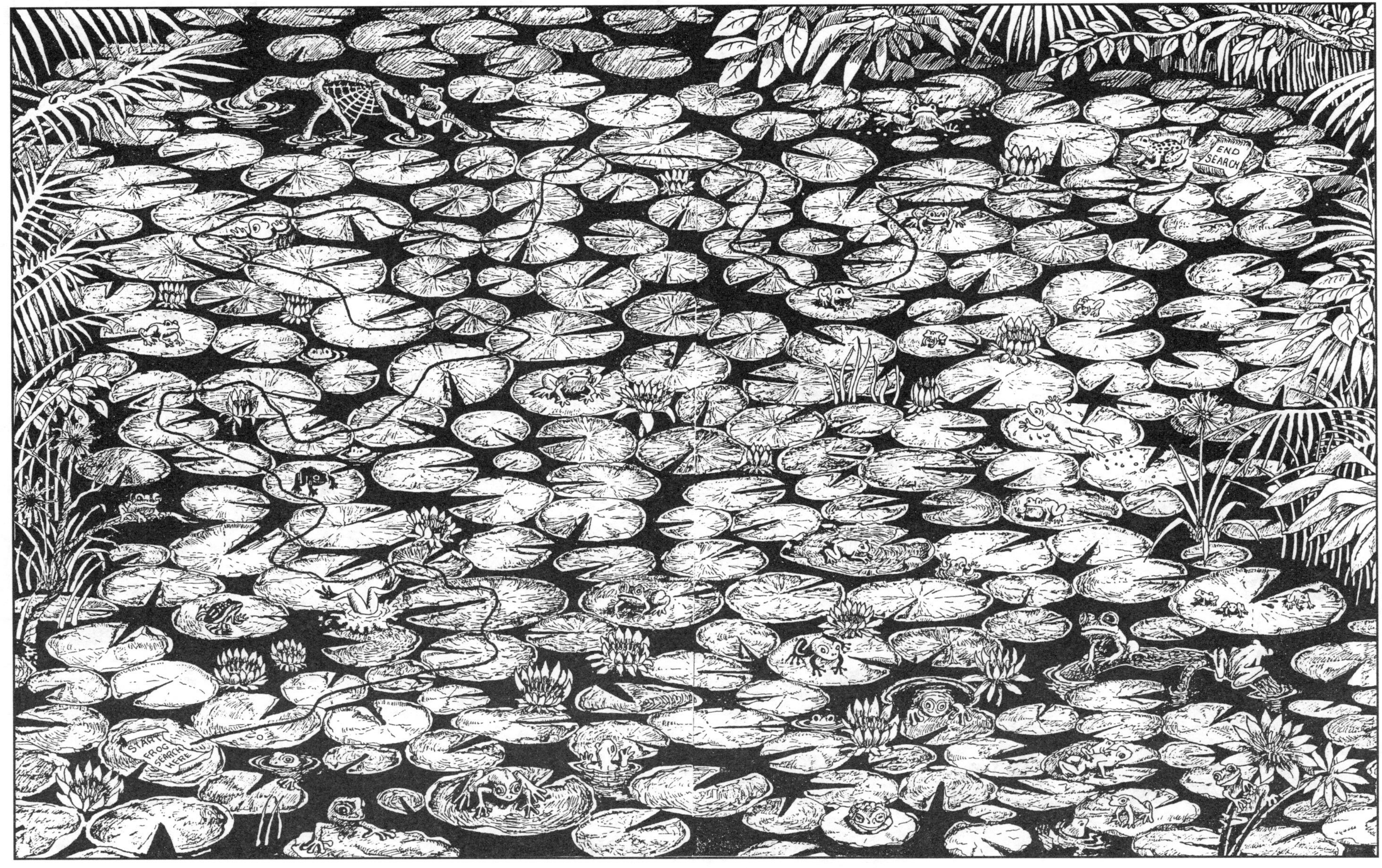

The Butterfly Chase

Stalking The Jaguar

The Road to the Jungle

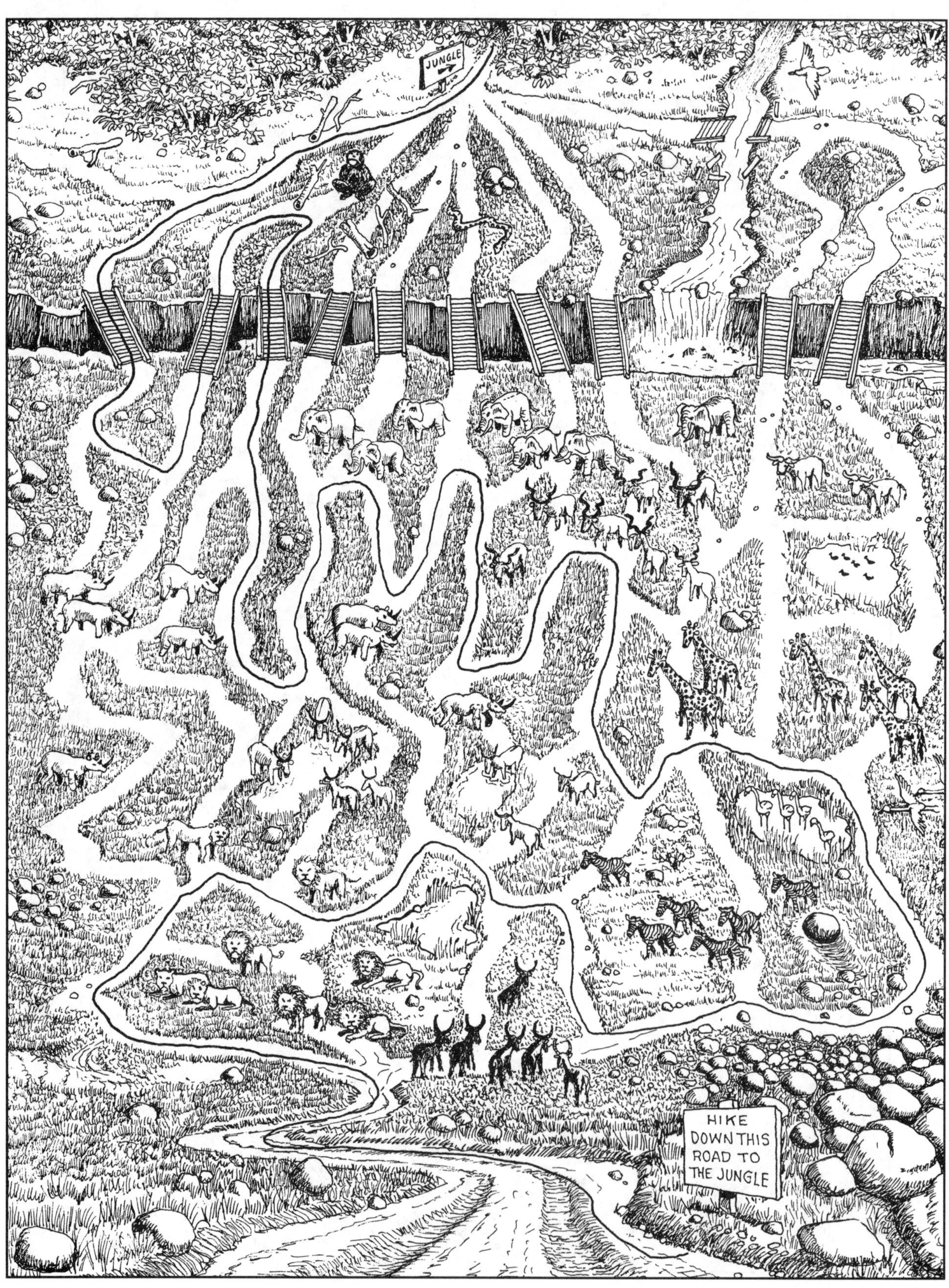

The Gorilla Family

Spiders, Spiders

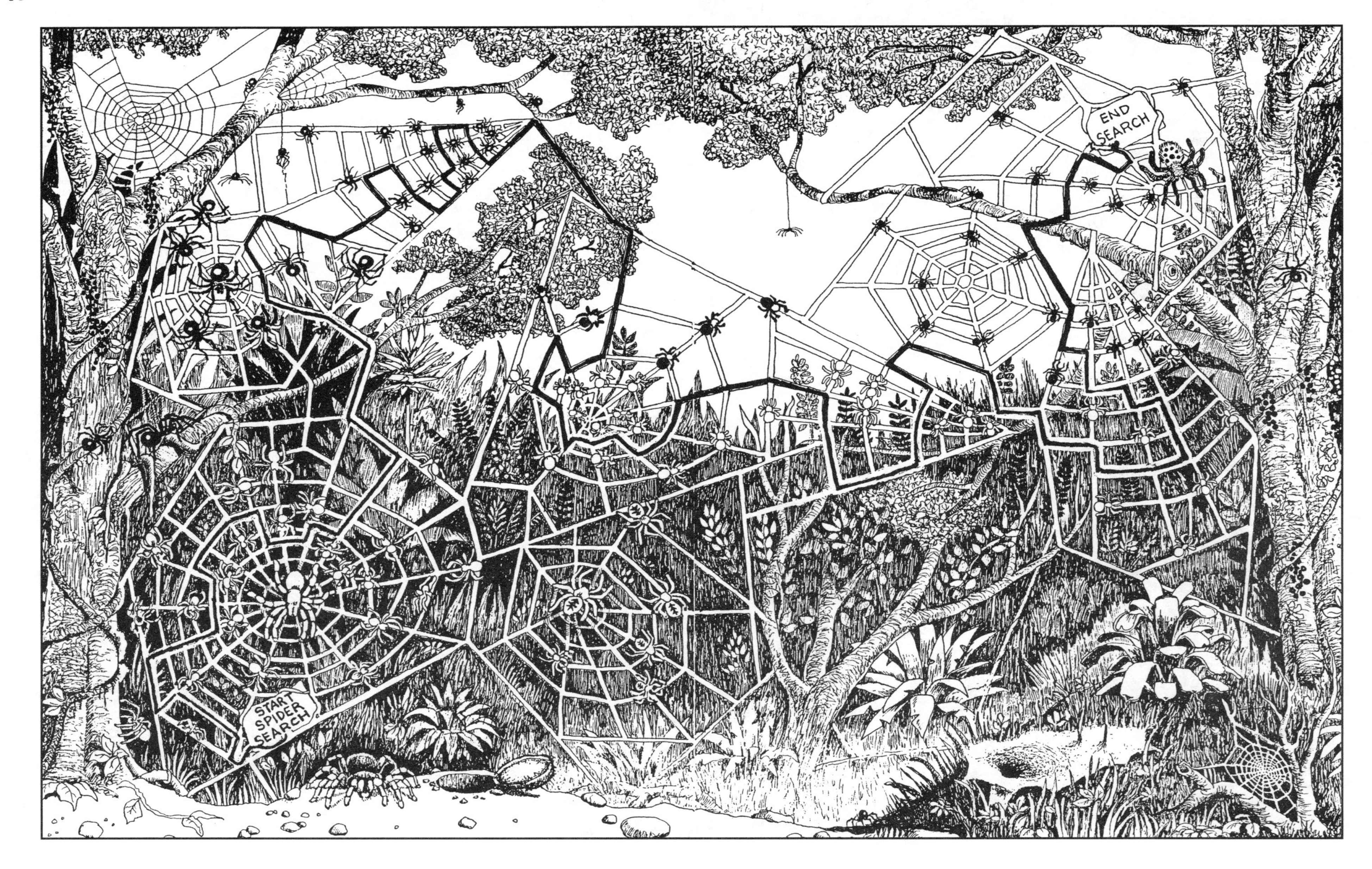

The Golden Potto

Jungle Photo Trip

The Elephant Herd

Monkey Business

A Clear Path

The Temple of Ankor

Inside the Temple

Snakes and Roots

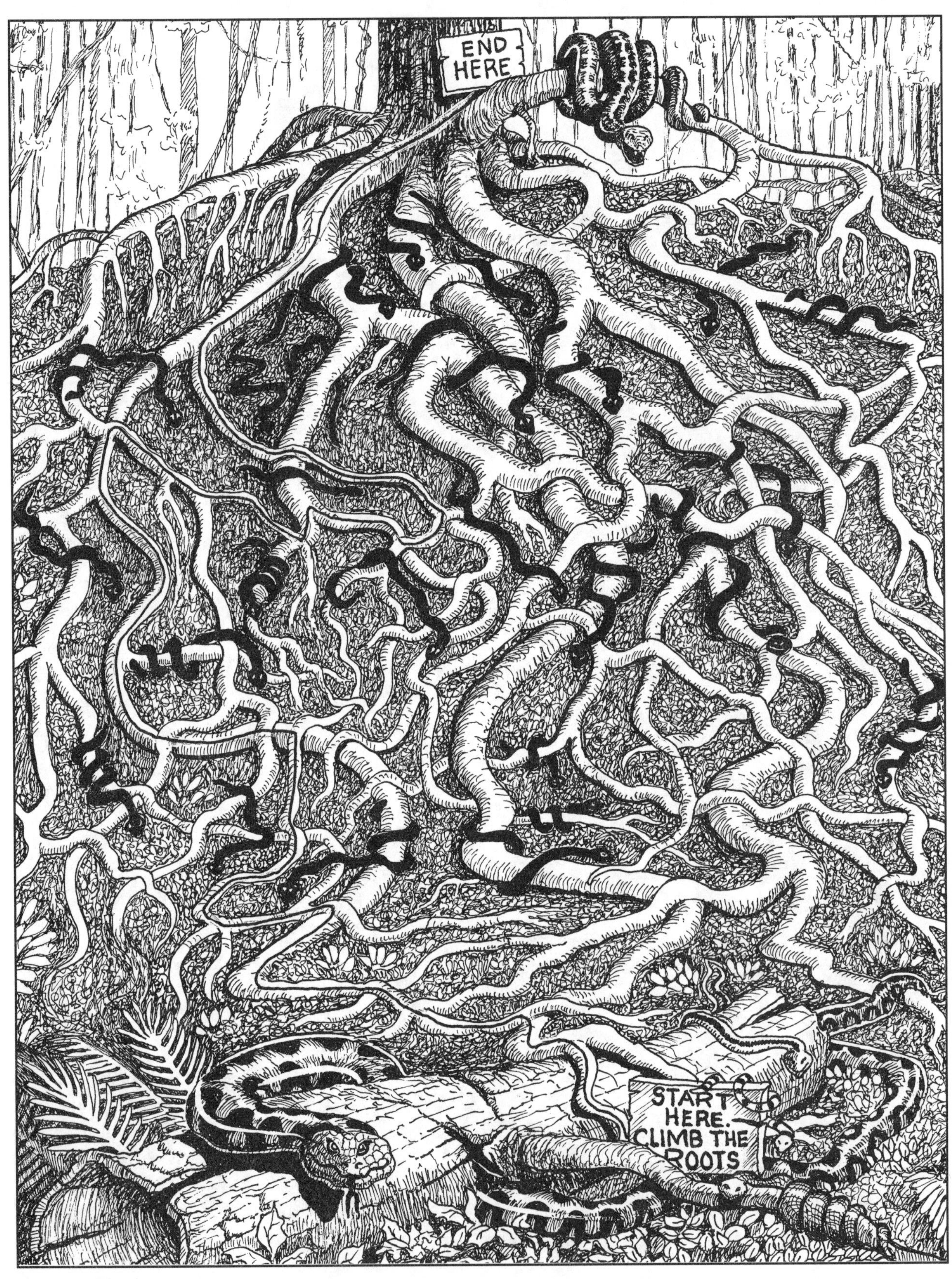

Looking for Lizards

The Crossroads

Out of the Jungle

INDEX

Numbers in bold refer to solutions to puzzles